Cob's W

Written by Vicky Butt

Illustrated by Sofia Cardoso

Cob has a web.

He can spin webs well.

Miss Muffet has a big picnic.

Clomp!

Clump!

Stop, Miss Muffet!
You will snap Cob's web!

Miss Muffet sits on the grass.

Snap!

Cob is sad, but he can fix the web.

Miss Muffet is back. She has a snack.

Stop, Miss Muffet!
You will bump Cob's web!

Cob is cross and he yells.

You must stop!

Miss Muffet drops her snack and runs off.

Cob can relax.

He spins the best web yet.

Talk about the story

Ask your child these questions:

1 What was Cob good at?

2 What did Miss Muffet do to Cob's web?

3 How did Cob feel about Miss Muffet?

4 How could Miss Muffet have behaved better?

5 Where have you seen a spider?

6 Are you frightened of spiders? Why/why not?

Can your child retell the story using their own words?